Reach
HIGHER

Practice Book

NATIONAL
GEOGRAPHIC
LEARNING

Australia · Brazil · Mexico · Singapore · United Kingdom · United States

NATIONAL GEOGRAPHIC LEARNING

National Geographic Learning,
a Cengage Company

Reach Higher Practice Book 2B

Publisher, Content-based English: Erik Gundersen

Associate Director, R&D: Barnaby Pelter

Senior Development Editors:
  Jacqueline Eu
  Ranjini Fonseka
  Kelsey Zhang

Development Editor: Rayne Ngoi

Editorial Assistant: Teh Chong Jin

Director of Global Marketing: Ian Martin

Heads of Regional Marketing:
  Charlotte Ellis (Europe, Middle East and Africa)
  Kiel Hamm (Asia)
  Irina Pereyra (Latin America)

Product Marketing Manager: David Spain

Senior Production Controller: Tan Jin Hock

Senior Media Researcher (Covers): Leila Hishmeh

Senior Designer: Lisa Trager

Director, Operations: Jason Seigel

Operations Support:
  Rebecca Barbush
  Drew Robertson
  Caroline Stephenson
  Nicholas Yeaton

Manufacturing Planner: Mary Beth Hennebury

Publishing Consultancy and Composition:
  MPS North America LLC

For permission to use material from this text or product, submit all requests online at **cengage.com/permissions**
Further permissions questions can be emailed to **permissionrequest@cengage.com**

ISBN-13: 978-0-357-36684-4

National Geographic Learning
200 Pier Four Blvd
Boston, MA 02210
USA

Locate your local office at **international.cengage.com/region**

Visit National Geographic Learning online at **ELTNGL.com**
Visit our corporate website at **www.cengage.com**

Printed in China
Print Number: 08   Print Year: 2023

Contents

Unit 5: Everything Changes

Unit 6: Better Together

Unit 7: Best Buddies

Unit 8: Our World

Name _____   Date _____

Everything Changes

Make a concept map with the answers to the Big Question:
Why is nature always changing?

Name _____   Date _____

My Favorite Story

Make a theme chart to tell the details about a favorite story.

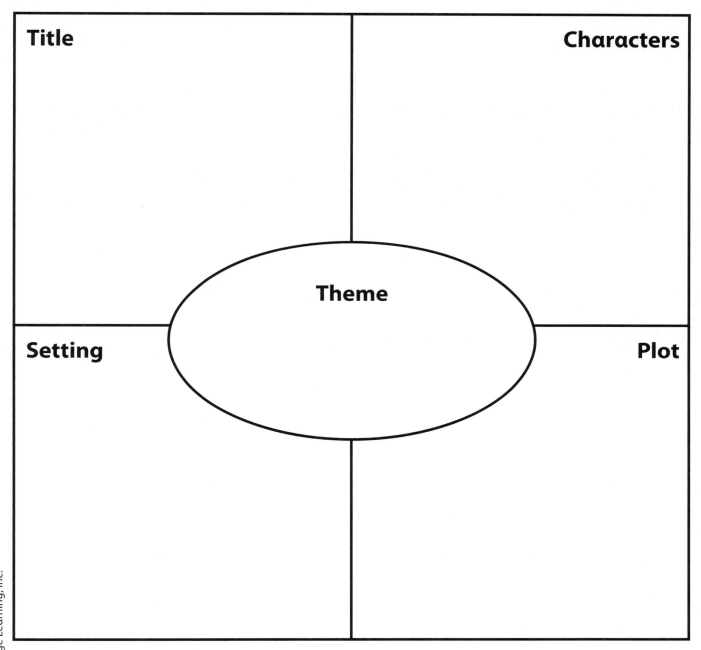

Title	Characters

Theme

Setting	Plot

Work with a partner to find the theme of your story.

Grammar

A Glorious Trip!

Grammar Rules Kinds of Sentences

Use a **period** at the end of a statement.	*Sunrise is at 6:00 a.m. this morning.*
Use an **exclamation mark** at the end of an exclamation.	*It's the most beautiful sunrise I've ever seen!*
Use a **period** or an **exclamation mark** at the end of a command.	*Bring me my camera. Come quickly before it's gone!*

Rewrite each sentence. Add a period or an exclamation mark.

1. We camped at the beach last night

_____

2. It was so exciting

_____

3. The sunrise and sunset were amazing

_____

4. Come with us next time

_____

5. Enjoy your meal

_____

Read your sentences to a partner. Use proper expression as you read exclamations and commands.

Key Points Reading

"When the Wind Stops"

Listen as your teacher reads. Follow with your finger.

1

A boy wonders why the day ends. His mother tells him that it is so a new night can begin. A new day begins in another place. She tells the boy nothing ever ends.

2

The boy wonders where the wind goes. His mother tells him it blows away to make the trees dance somewhere else. She tells him after a storm the rain goes back to the clouds.

3

The mother tells the boy that the end of autumn is the beginning of winter. The end of winter is the beginning of spring.

4

The boy learns that nature goes on and on. Nothing ever ends.

Grammar

Is It OK to be Negative?

Grammar Rules Kinds of Sentences

A question asks something. It ends with a **question mark**.

Example: *Is that your shadow?*

A negative sentence uses a negative word, like **not**.

It usually ends with a **period**.

Example: *That is **not** my shadow.*

For each sentence, underline the end punctuation. Then circle what type of sentence it is.

1. When does the moon appear? (negative sentence/ question)

2. It does not appear during the day. (negative sentence/ question)

3. Can you see the moon at night? (negative sentence/ question)

4. We will not miss it. (negative sentence/ question)

5. Do you want to learn more about the moon? (negative sentence/question)

 Tell a partner about the moon. Include one question and one negative sentence.

© Cengage Learning, Inc.

"When the Wind Stops"

Use clues from the story to figure out the theme.

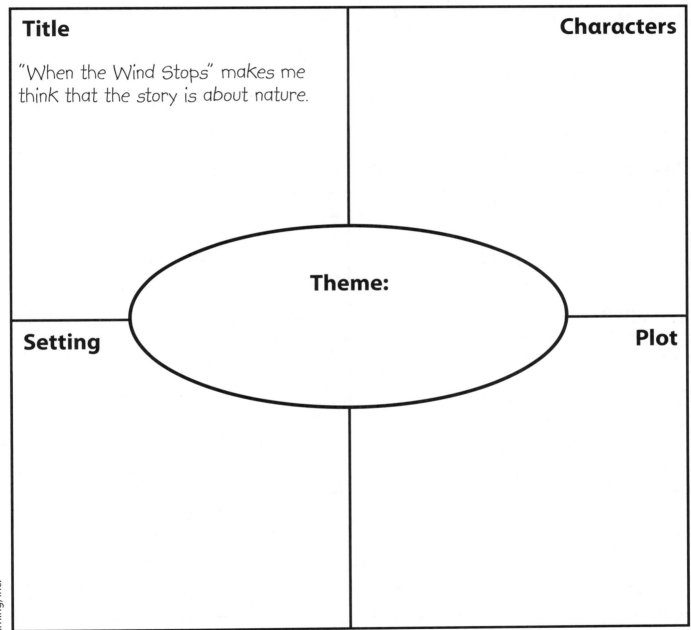

Title

"When the Wind Stops" makes me think that the story is about nature.

Characters

Theme:

Setting

Plot

Share your theme chart with a partner. Tell about the clues you used.

Name _____ Date _____

Vowel Sounds and Spellings:
air, are, ear

ch<u>air</u>   h<u>are</u>   b<u>ear</u>

Read each word. Circle the word that goes with each picture.

1. have hair heat	**2.** pair peer pier
3. term tear tire	**4.** square squeak spare
5. part pear pore	**6.** stair stop stand

Work with a partner. Take turns reading the sentence and answering the question.

Can you eat a pear on the stair?

Fluency

"When the Wind Stops"

Use this passage to practice reading with proper expression.

The bright sun had shone all day, and now the day   11

was coming to an end. The sun sank lower into the   22

glowing pink clouds. The little boy was sorry to see the   33

day end.   35

From "When the Wind Stops," page 14

Expression

B ☐ Does not read with feeling   A ☐ Reads with appropriate feeling for most content

I ☐ Reads with some feeling, but does not match content   AH ☐ Reads with appropriate feeling for all content

Accuracy and Rate Formula

Use the formula to measure a reader's accuracy and rate while reading aloud.

$$\underline{\hspace{3cm}} - \underline{\hspace{3cm}} = \underline{\hspace{3cm}}$$

words attempted   number of errors   words correct per minute
in one minute   (wcpm)

"Day and Night"

Use the K-W-L-Q chart to record your ideas as you read "Day and Night."

What I know	What I want to learn	What I learned	Questions I still have

With a partner, share what you learned about night and day. Then write questions you still have in the last column.

Respond and Extend

Compare Author's Purpose

Show why Charlotte Zolotow wrote "When the Wind Stops." Compare it to why Glen Phelan wrote "Day and Night."

Charlotte Zolotow	Glen Phelan
• to tell about patterns in nature	• to explain how day becomes night

Tell a partner which selection you liked better. Explain your favorite author's purpose for writing.

Grammar

Build a Sentence

1. Play with a partner.

2. Use the words below to build sentences. Write a question, a statement, a command, and an exclamation.

3. Begin with a capital letter. Add an end mark.

4. The player who first writes all four types of sentences correctly wins.

Is/is	night	beautiful
The/the	Do/do	star
your	see	shadow
Come/come	get	you
Are/are	book	That/that

_____

_____

_____

_____

Name ______________________ Date ______________

Thinking Map

Compare and Contrast

Complete the comparison chart below.

Picture cards	How they are alike	How they are different
Picture card 1: ______		
Picture card 2: ______		

Share your chart with a partner. Tell how your picture cards are alike and different.

Grammar

The Seasons

Grammar Rules Yes/No Questions

Some questions have **Yes** or **No** answers. They start with a verb like **Is**, **Are**, **Do**, and **Does**. They end with a question mark (**?**).

Question	Answer
Are you cold**?**	**Yes**, I am cold.
Do you like snow**?**	**No**, I do not like snow.

Write an answer to each question. Use "yes" or "no" in your answer.

1. Is winter a season?

_____

2. Do leaves fall in spring?

_____

3. Are there four seasons?

_____

4. Does it snow in summer?

_____

▬▬▬ **Write your own question and have a partner answer it.**

Key Points Reading

"What Makes the Seasons?"

Listen as your teacher reads. Follow with your finger.

Spring melts the snow. It brings rain and leaves begin to bud. Seeds sprout and grow. But spring cannot stay. It leaves on a summer day.

Summer brings the growing season. Flowers bloom and trees are green. The days are long, warm, and sunny.

When the summer ends, autumn days begin. Cold winds blow. The green leaves change colors and fall from the trees.

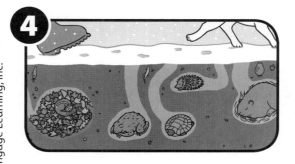

Winter brings snow. Everything sleeps. Trees and seeds rest. Animals hibernate.
The seasons change because of Earth's yearly trip around the sun. When it is summer in one part of the world, it is winter in another.

Grammar

Question Word Rivet

Grammar Rules Questions

Questions that ask for more information often start with **Who**, **What**, **Where**, **Why**, **When**, or **How**.

Who *asks about a person.*	**Why** *asks for a reason.*
What *asks about a thing.*	**When** *asks about a time.*
Where *asks about a place.*	**How** *asks about the way things happen.*

Each sentence needs a question word. Spell the question word that belongs with each sentence by filling in the blanks. Work with a partner to see who can complete the word first.

1. __ h __ tells you about weather in your city?

2. W __ __ did it snow early this year?

3. __ __ w does a thermometer work?

4. __ __ e __ will spring begin?

5. W __ __ __ happens when ice melts?

6. __ h __ __ __ is the hottest place on Earth?

"What Makes the Seasons?"

Complete the comparison chart below. Show how the seasons are alike and different.

	Spring	Summer	Fall	Winter
Leaves	sprout			
Raindrops	fall			
Snow	melts			
Days	get longer			

Use the information from the chart to tell your partner how the seasons are alike and different.

Silent Consonants: *gn, kn*

g̲nome   k̲nee

Read each word. Circle the word that goes with each picture.

1. gnome knit knight	**2.** gnu knee glue
3. knock gnat get	**4.** kick clock knock
5. align light alive	**6.** knit gnat knight

Work with a partner. Take turns reading the sentence and pointing to the objects.

Find a gnu, a knight, and a gnat.

Fluency

"What Makes the Seasons?"

Use this passage to practice reading with proper intonation.

Winter is a time for sleep.	6
Trees are resting. Seeds will keep.	12
Many creatures sleep and wait.	17
Winter's time to hibernate.	21
But what controls the season's change?	27
And what makes weather rearrange?	32
Earth's yearly trip around the sun	38
affects the seasons one by one.	44

From "What Makes the Seasons?" pages 55–56

Intonation

B ☐ Does not vary intonation or use end marks to determine whether voice should rise or fall during reading

A ☐ Varies intonation; usually uses end marks (questions marks and periods) to determine whether voice should rise or fall during reading

I ☐ Sometimes varies intonation, using end marks (question marks and periods) to determine whether voice should rise or fall during reading

AH ☐ Varies intonation; always uses end marks to determine whether voice should rise or fall during reading

Accuracy and Rate Formula

Use the formula to measure a reader's accuracy and rate while reading aloud.

$$\underline{\hspace{4cm}} - \underline{\hspace{4cm}} = \underline{\hspace{4cm}}$$

words attempted in one minute	number of errors	words correct per minute (wcpm)

Name _____ Date _____

"A Winter Wonder"

Make fact cards about frogs. Write the topic, state a fact, and draw a picture on each card.

That's Amazing!

Fact Card 1

An amazing fact about _____

is _____

_____

_____ .

Picture

That's Amazing!

Fact Card 2

An amazing fact about _____

is _____

_____

_____ .

Picture

 **Share your cards with a partner and compare facts.**

© Cengage Learning, Inc.

Compare Genres

Use the Venn diagram to tell how "What Makes the Seasons?" and "A Winter Wonder" are alike and different.

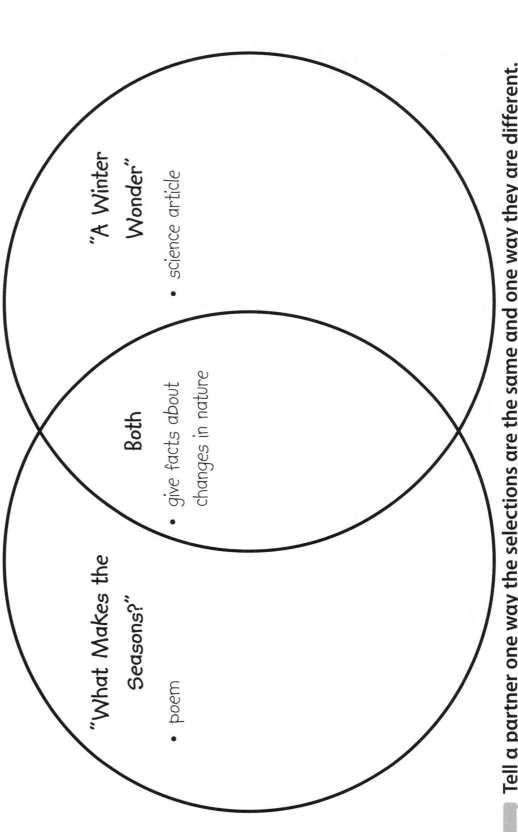

"A Winter Wonder"
- science article

Both
- give facts about changes in nature

"What Makes the Seasons?"
- poem

Tell a partner one way the selections are the same and one way they are different.

Grammar

Wonderful Winter

Grammar Rules Questions

- A **question** ends with a question mark (**?**).
- The **answer** to a question ends with a period (**.**).

Add the correct punctuation to each of the sentences.

1. Who likes winter as much as I do

2. Many people think winter is a great season

3. Is it because there are fun things to do in the snow

4. Yes, I think it is

5. What are your favorite winter activities

6. I like to sled, ski, and build forts in the snow

7. Do you ever get cold in winter

8. No, I don't get cold because I dress warmly

 Work with a partner to ask and answer two questions about seasons.

Name _____ Date _____

Organization

Writing is organized when it is easy to follow. All the ideas make sense together and flow from one idea to the next in an order that fits the writer's audience and purpose.

	Is the writing well-organized? Does it fit the writer's purpose?	**Does the writing flow?**
4 Wow!	❑ The writing is very well-organized ❑ It clearly fits the writer's purpose.	❑ The writing is smooth and logical. ❑ Each sentence flows into the next one.
3 Ahh.	❑ Most of the writing is organized. ❑ It mostly fits the writer's purpose.	❑ Most of the writing is smooth. ❑ There are only a few sentences that do not flow logically.
2 Hmm.	❑ The writing is not well-organized. ❑ It fits the writer's purpose somewhat.	❑ Some of the writing is smooth. ❑ Many sentences do not flow smoothly.
1 Huh?	❑ The writing is not organized at all. ❑ It does not fit the writer's purpose.	❑ The writing is not smooth. ❑ The sentences do not flow smoothly or logically.

Comparison Chart

Complete the chart to compare two seasons.

	Season: _____	Season: _____
Temperature		
Weather		
Sports		

Writing Project

Revise

Use revision marks to make changes to these paragraphs. Look for:

- well-organized ideas
- words that show comparisons
- correct spelling
- capitalization

Revision Marks	
∧	Add
ℱ	Take out
⬭⌐	Move to here

Winter and Summer

Winter and summer are my favorite seasons.

I like the hot weather in summer. I can swim at the beach. I can't swim in the winter. I can wear sandals and shorts. In winter, I need warm clothes.

The cold weather in winter lets me do winter activities. I love to ski and ice skate. Both winter and summer are fun. It's also fun to build a snowman.

Writing Project

Edit and Proofread

Use revision marks to edit and
proofread these paragraphs. Look for:

- spellings with *ie* or *ei*
- different kinds of sentences and
  their punctuation
- apostrophes

Revision Marks	
∧	Add
℘	Take out
⬭⌐	Move to here
⬭SP	Check spelling
⊙	Insert period
?∧	Insert question mark
౨	Insert apostrophe

Weather Opposites

I live in Colorado. Summer and winter are very different here.

In the summer, the weather is hot, and I love hot weather? I go to

the lake with my freinds. We play volleyball and swim. We have fun

during summer?

Winter is very different. It can get very cold. If the temperature

gets in the 30's, we think it's warm. Why do I love winter! The snow is

pretty. My nieghbors' house has a warm fireplace. When my family

visits them, we drink hot cocoa at my friends house.

Winter and summer are very different, but I like them both.

Unit Concept Map

Better Together

**Make a concept map with the answers to the Big Question:
Why is it good to work together?**

Why is it good to work together?

Story Elements

Use a story map to tell about the characters, setting, and plot of a story.

Character:

Character:

Setting:

Plot:

Event 1: _____
_____

Event 2: _____
_____

Event 3: _____
_____

Use your story map to tell a partner a story about being part of a team.

Grammar

We Care and Share!

Grammar Rules Subject Pronouns

Pronouns take the place of nouns. Use these **subject pronouns** to tell who or what does the action.

Example: **Tony and I** like to work. **We** work together.

One	More than one
I	we
you	you
he, she, it	they

Write the correct pronoun to complete each sentence.

1. Jon likes to help. _____ helps his mom with the dishes.

2. Kate and Sanjay like to give. _____ give clothes to a shelter.

3. The truck picks up the clothes. _____ is a big truck.

4. Toby, Jill, and I like to share. _____ share our toys with one another.

5. Maya likes teamwork. _____ works best with others.

▶ **Write your own sentence using a subject pronoun. Share your sentence with a partner.**

© Cengage Learning, Inc.

"Domino Soup"

Listen as your teacher reads. Follow with your finger.

1  Maria wants to make a welcome dinner for the new neighbors. She thinks everyone can share a little food. But no one wants to share.

2  Maria has an idea. She asks Grandpa for a domino. She wants to make Domino Soup. Everyone follows Maria to watch her make the soup.

3  Maria cooks the domino in a pot of water. She says it smells good. No one else can smell anything. Maria wants an onion to make the soup smell better. The grocer gets one. Soon, everyone is bringing things.

4  The new neighbors smell the soup. They knock at the door. Maria and her friends invite them to have some soup. The neighbors say the neighborhood is very big-hearted.

Grammar

Soup for Us

Grammar Rules Object Pronouns

Pronouns take the place of nouns. Use **object pronouns** after action words or after words like *at, with, for, to,* or *of.*

Example: *I want to make soup for **the neighbors**. I cook for **them**.*

One	More than one
me	us
you	you
him, her, it	them

Circle the object pronoun that takes the place of the noun.

1. Maria gets a **pot** and places it on the stove.

2. The butcher sees **Maria** and asks her if the soup needs chicken.

3. A neighbor brings **potatoes** and adds them to the pot.

4. Maria likes to cook for **Grandpa**. Maria gives some soup to him.

5. **My friend and I** see the baker. The baker shares her bread with us.

Use an object pronoun in a new sentence. Then read your sentence to a partner.

Name _____ Date _____

"Domino Soup"

Make a story map for "Domino Soup."

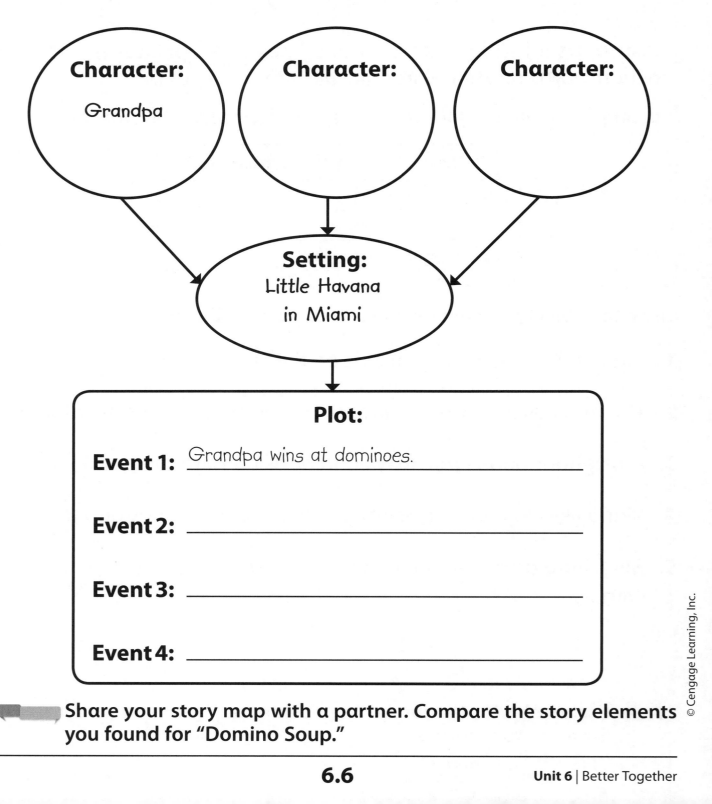

Character:
Grandpa

Character:

Character:

Setting:
Little Havana
in Miami

Plot:

Event 1: Grandpa wins at dominoes. _____

Event 2: _____

Event 3: _____

Event 4: _____

Share your story map with a partner. Compare the story elements you found for "Domino Soup."

© Cengage Learning, Inc.

Phonics Practice

Silent Consonants: *mb, wr*

la<u>mb</u>   <u>wr</u>ist

Read each word. Write the word that completes each sentence.

1. This is my _____.  thumb comb tube	**2.** A _____ is a useful tool. 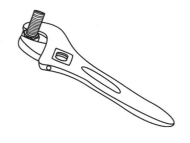 wrench vase wrap
3. I am a _____.  knitter writer climber	**4.** Look at the tree _____.  lamb wrist limb

Work with a partner. Take turns reading the sentence and pointing to the objects.

Find a writer, a limb, and a thumb.

"Domino Soup"

Use this passage to practice reading with proper expression.
Do not read the character names aloud.

BAKER:	I hear there's a new family	6
	moving in next week.	10
NEIGHBOR 1:	I have a great idea!	15
	We should welcome them to the neighborhood	22
	with a big feast!	26
NEIGHBOR 2:	I'll bring the domino!	30

From "Domino Soup," page 98

Expression

B ☐ Does not read with feeling.   A ☐ Reads with appropriate feeling for most content.

I ☐ Reads with some feeling, but does not match content.   AH ☐ Reads with appropriate feeling for all content.

Accuracy and Rate Formula

Use the formula to measure a reader's accuracy and rate while reading aloud.

_____ − _____ = _____
words attempted   number of errors   words correct per minute
in one minute   (wcpm)

"Stone Soup"

Complete the journal with a partner as you read "Stone Soup." Write your ideas in column 1. Have a partner write ideas in column 2.

What I think	What my partner thinks
Page _____ _____ _____ _____	_____ _____ _____ _____
Page _____ _____ _____ _____	_____ _____ _____ _____
Page _____ _____ _____ _____	_____ _____ _____ _____

Talk to a partner about how your opinions are the same and different.

Respond and Extend

Compare Two Versions of the Same Story

Use a comparison chart to show how "Domino Soup" and "Stone Soup" are alike and different.

	"Domino Soup"	**"Stone Soup"**
Type of story	play	song
Characters		
Setting		
Plot		

Tell a partner how the two versions of the story are the same and different.

Grammar

The Pronoun Game

1. Play with a partner.
2. Spin the spinner.
3. Name a pronoun to replace the words in the space.
4. Say a sentence using the pronoun.
5. Color in the space.
6. Play until all the spaces are colored in.

Make a Spinner

1. Place one loop of a paper clip over the center of the circle.
2. Push a sharp pencil through the loop and the paper.
3. Spin the paper clip around the pencil.

Name _____   Date _____

Main Idea

Make a main idea diagram to tell about a time you worked with someone to reach a goal.

Detail:	Detail:

Main idea:

© Cengage Learning, Inc.

Grammar

Our Class Project

Grammar Rules Possessive Adjectives

A **possessive adjective** always comes before a noun. It tells who or what owns something.

Example: *We care about **our** education.*

Singular	Plural
my	our
your	your
his, her, its	their

Write the possessive adjective that completes each sentence. Then circle the noun it describes.

1. This project belongs to all of you. This is __your__ (project)

2. This dream belongs to me. This is _____ dream.

3. This is the boy's plan. This is _____ plan.

4. This is the project's result. This is _____ result.

5. These are the students' skills. These are _____ skills.

6. My classmates and I have these goals. These are _____ goals.

> Use a possessive adjective in a sentence about something that belongs to one or more people in your class. Share your sentence with a partner.

Name _____   Date _____

"Saving an Island"

Listen as your teacher reads. Follow with your finger.

1

Pemba Island is a beautiful island near Tanzania. It is very fertile and people grow many crops there.

2

Over the years, the population grew. People cut down lots of trees to clear more land for farming. Mangroves were cut down too, and this resulted in less fish for people to eat.

3

Community leaders were worried. They started to collect seeds and grow new plants. Bees helped pollinate the plants.

4

More than two million trees were planted over 10 years. Now there are more trees, and farmers have more crops to sell. Everyone works together to save Pemba Island.

Grammar

Our Class Fundraiser

Grammar Rules Possessive Pronouns

- A **possessive pronoun** shows ownership.
- **Possessive pronouns** do not come before nouns. They stand alone.
  Example: *That plan is **theirs**.*

Singular	Plural
mine	ours
yours	yours
his, hers	theirs

Fill in the blank with the correct possessive pronoun.

1. This idea for a fundraiser belongs to us. The idea is __ours__.

2. This is her plan for the event. This plan is _____.

3. You and Mario have the lists of what we will need. The lists are _____.

4. This chart belongs to him. This chart is _____.

5. These are their tools. These tools are _____.

6. This is my schedule for the event. This schedule is _____.

7. This is your opportunity. This opportunity is _____.

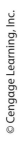

Write a sentence that uses a possessive pronoun to tell who owns or has something. Share the sentence with a partner.

Vocabulary

Vocabulary Bingo

Play Bingo using the Key Words from this unit.

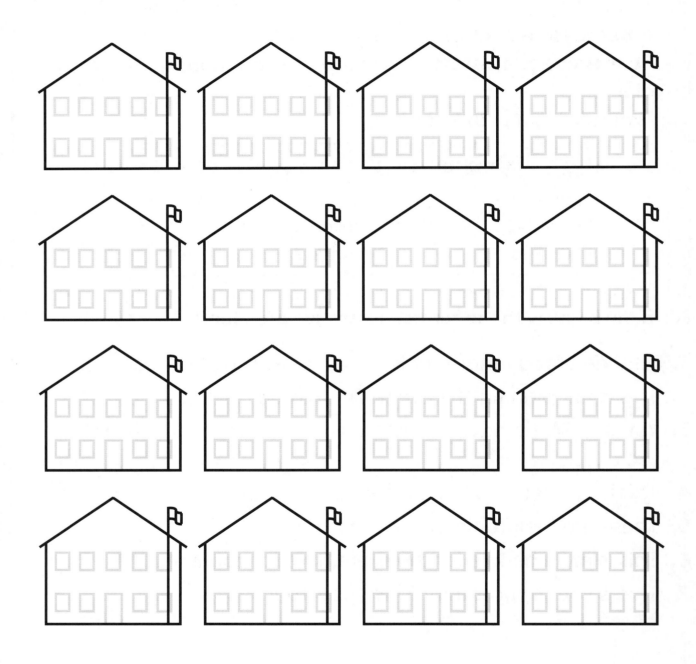

Reread and Retell

"Saving an Island"

Make a main idea diagram for "Saving an Island."

Detail:	Detail:
They cut down the trees on the island.	

Main idea:

🔲 **Share your main idea diagram with a partner. See if you found the same main idea.**

Phonics Practice

Vowel Sounds and Spellings: *oo, ui*

m<u>oo</u>n

j<u>ui</u>ce

Read each word. Circle the word that goes with each picture.

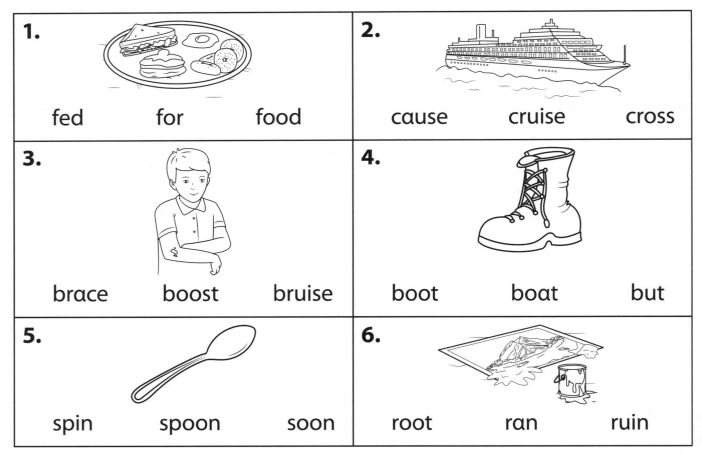

1. fed for food	**2.** cause cruise cross
3. brace boost bruise	**4.** boot boat but
5. spin spoon soon	**6.** root ran ruin

Work with a partner. Take turns reading the sentence and pointing to the objects.

Find a bruise, a spoon, and a boot.

Fluency

"Saving an Island"

Use this passage to practice reading with proper phrasing.

Pemba Island is very fertile,   5

and the local people   9

grow many crops.   12

Mangroves and lagoons   15

line the coast.   18

Tourists come to visit   22

its beautiful beaches   25

and see colorful fish   29

in the sea.   32

From "Saving an Island," page 123

Phrasing

B ☐ Rarely pauses while reading the text   A ☐ Frequently pauses at appropriate points in the text

I ☐ Occasionally pauses while reading the text   AH ☐ Consistently pauses at all appropriate points in the text

Accuracy and Rate Formula

Use the formula to measure a reader's accuracy and rate while reading aloud.

_____ – _____ = _____
words attempted   number of errors   words correct per minute
in one minute   (wcpm)

Compare Texts

Use the comparison chart to show how "Saving an Island" and "Mi Barrio" are alike and different.

	"Saving an Island"	**"Mi Barrio"**
It is in an urban community.		✓
It is in a rural community.	✓	
The community members help each other.		
The children help their community, too.		
The selection is illustrated with photographs.		
It is a true story.		

▬▬▬ Compare your chart with a partner's. See if you found the same information.

© Cengage Learning, Inc.

Grammar

Possessive Pronoun Concentration

1. Play with 2 or 3 people. Copy all the words below onto separate cards.

2. Mix the cards up and put them face down.

3. Turn over two cards. If the possessive pronoun card matches the noun card, keep both cards. If the two cards do not match, turn them face down again in the same place.

4. The player with the most cards at the end wins.

Nouns			
Lee and Ana's notes	Our project	Samir and your plans	Lilu's marker
My goals	Your skill	Jackson's paper	

Possessive Pronouns			
Mine	Yours	Ours	Theirs
His	Hers	Yours	

Use three of the nouns above. Tell a partner something about you.

Name _____   Date _____

Organization

Writing is organized when it is easy to follow. All the ideas make sense together and flow from one idea to the next in an order that fits the writer's audience and purpose.

	Is the writing well-organized? Does it fit the writer's purpose?	Does the writing flow?
4 Wow!	❑ The writing is very well-organized. ❑ It clearly fits the writer's purpose.	❑ The writing is smooth and logical. ❑ Each sentence flows into the next one.
3 Ahh.	❑ Most of the writing is organized. ❑ It mostly fits the writer's purpose.	❑ Most of the writing is smooth. ❑ There are only a few sentences that do not flow logically.
2 Hmm.	❑ The writing is not well-organized. ❑ It fits the writer's purpose somewhat.	❑ Some of the writing is smooth. ❑ Many sentences do not flow smoothly.
1 Huh?	❑ The writing is not organized at all. ❑ It does not fit the writer's purpose.	❑ The writing is not smooth. ❑ The sentences do not flow smoothly or logically.

Name _____ Date _____

Story Map

Complete the story map for your story.

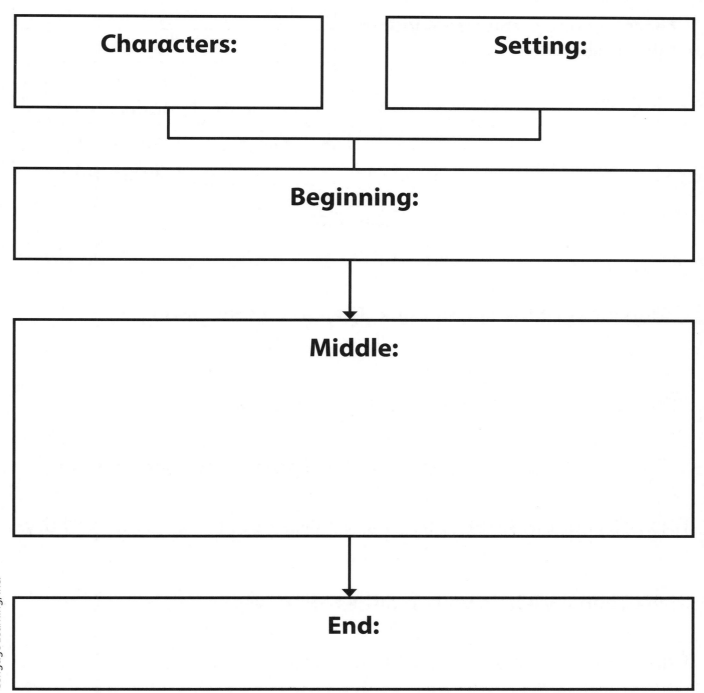

Characters:

Setting:

Beginning:

Middle:

End:

Writing Project

Revise

Use revision marks to make changes to the story. Look for:

- **character and setting descriptions**
- **missing details**

Revision Marks	
∧	Add
ℐ	Take out
⸌⸍	Insert quotation marks
⫪	Insert new paragraph

Show Time

Tina looks at the kitchen sink. There are many dishes.

"It's your turn to do the dishes," says Tina's dad.

The movie starts in fifteen minutes. There are too many dishes!

Tina asks her big sister to help. "I will wash the dishes if you will dry

them. Then I will help you do dishes tomorrow."

Tina rushes next door to her friend's house. At her friend's, she sits

down to watch the movie.

Writing Project

Edit and Proofread

Use revision marks to edit and proofread this story. Look for:

- **spelling of they're/their/there; its/it's; your/you're**
- **pronoun agreement**
- **punctuation**

Revision Marks	
∧	Add
৵	Take out
⊙	Insert period
?	Insert question mark
!	Insert exclamation point
⌄	Insert comma
⌄	Insert apostrophe

A Clever Cat Trick

"Its time to take your cat to the vet, " Gabby's mom said. "Put

Buddy in their pet carrier."

Gabby looked everywhere for my cat. "Buddy! Where are you."

Gabby found Buddy hiding under the bed. "How will I get him out?"

Her had an idea.

Buddy loves cheese? Gabby made a cheese trail from the bed

into the pet carrier Slowly Buddy came out. He ate all the cheese

until he was inside the carrier.

Now there ready to take Buddy for his checkup at the vet.

Unit Concept Map

Best Buddies

Make a concept map with answers to the Big Question:
How do living things depend on each other?

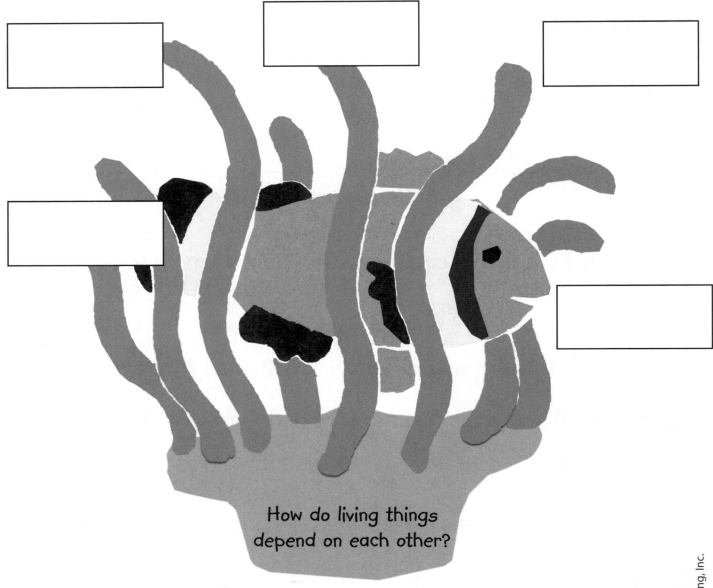

How do living things depend on each other?

Characters' Motives

Make a character map for the animal in your story.

Character	What the character does	Why the character does it

Tell a partner your story. Then share your character map and talk about the character's motives.

Name _____ Date _____

Grammar

Food Chains

Grammar Rules Regular Past Tense Verbs

Use the **past tense** to tell about an action that has already happened. Add **-ed** to most verbs when you talk about a past action.

Examples: | jump | + | **ed** | = | jump**ed** |

| wish | + | **ed** | = | wish**ed** |

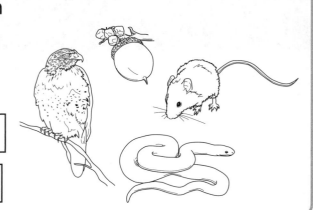

Write the past tense form of each verb. Then read each sentence aloud.

1. | chew | The mouse _____ on an acorn.

2. | want | A snake _____ to catch the mouse.

3. | hunt | A hawk _____ the snake.

4. | munch | A rabbit _____ on the grass.

5. | look | A hawk _____ at the rabbit.

6. | leap | The rabbit _____ away from the hawk.

 Choose a verb from one of the boxes and make a new sentence. Have a partner use the verb in the past tense and say the sentence again.

© Cengage Learning, Inc.

Name _____   Date _____

"Go to Sleep, Gecko!"

Listen as your teacher reads. Follow with your finger.

1 Gecko wakes Elephant in the middle of the night. He can't sleep. The fireflies are blinking their lights around his house. He wants Elephant to make them stop.

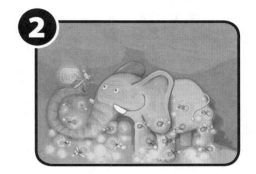

2 The fireflies tell Elephant that they blink their lights to keep people safe. People can fall into the holes that Rain makes in the road.

3 Gecko wakes Elephant up again. Elephant says Gecko must live with the fireflies because of Rain. Gecko asks Elephant to make Rain stop.

4 Rain tells Elephant that he makes puddles for mosquitoes. Without mosquitoes, Gecko would not have anything to eat. Elephant reminds Gecko that the whole world is connected.

Grammar

Irregular Past Tense Verbs Game

1. To play, take turns with a partner.

2. Toss a marker onto the game board.

3. Say the past tense form of the verb you land on. Then use the verb in a sentence to tell about the past.

am	go
is	goes
are	do

Name _____ Date _____

"Go to Sleep, Gecko!"

Make a character map for the characters in "Go to Sleep, Gecko!"

Character	What the character does	Why the character does it
Gecko	He complains about the fireflies.	He can't sleep.

 Share your character map with a partner. Compare what you wrote about the characters in "Go to Sleep, Gecko!"

Phonics Practice

Vowel Sounds and Spellings: *ue, ew*

gl<u>ue</u>

scr<u>ew</u>

Read each word. Circle the word that goes with each picture.

1.	2.
few flew flow	crew globe clue
3.	**4.**
step stew stool	Sue Sam Peter
5.	**6.**
now new grew	threw thread throne

Work with a partner. Take turns reading the sentence.

Can a clue help Sue make some stew?

Fluency

"Go to Sleep, Gecko!"

Use this passage to practice reading with proper expression.

Gecko thought.	2
If Elephant told Rain to stop raining,	9
there would be no holes and puddles in the road.	19
If there were no holes and puddles in the road,	29
the fireflies would stop flashing their lights . . .	36
but Gecko would have nothing to eat!	43
"Gecko," said Elephant.	46
"This world is all connected.	51
Some things you just have to put up with.	60
Now go home and go to sleep."	67

From "Go to Sleep, Gecko!" pages 172–173

Expression

B ☐ Does not read with feeling.

I ☐ Reads with some feeling, but does not match content.

A ☐ Reads with appropriate feeling for most content.

AH ☐ Reads with appropriate feeling for all content.

Accuracy and Rate Formula

Use the formula to measure a reader's accuracy and rate while reading aloud.

_____ – _____ = _____
words attempted   number of errors   words correct per minute
in one minute   (wcpm)

© Cengage Learning, Inc.

Reading Options

"Enric Sala: Marine Ecologist"

Use Word Detective cards to write about words from the selection.

 WORD DETECTIVE

New Word: _____

What I think it means: _____

_____

🔍 Clues: _____

_____

📖 Definition: _____

_____

_____

WORD DETECTIVE

New Word: _____

What I think it means: _____

_____

🔍 Clues: _____

_____

📖 Definition: _____

_____

Share a word you learned with a partner. Describe what it means.

Compare Genres

Complete a comparison chart to compare "Go to Sleep, Gecko!" and "Enric Sala: Marine Ecologist."

"Go to Sleep, Gecko!"	"Enric Sala: Marine Ecologist"
• folk tale • fiction	• profile • nonfiction

Use your comparison chart to tell a partner how "Go to Sleep, Gecko!" and "Enric Sala: Marine Ecologist" are alike and different.

Grammar

Gecko in the Past

Grammar Rules Past Tense Verbs

- Add **-ed** to most verbs when you talk about a past action.
  Example: *kick* + **-ed** = *kick**ed***
- Some verbs have special forms to show an action in the past.
  Example: *say* ➔ *said*

Circle the correct verb form.

1. Gecko want/(wanted) to sleep that night.

2. Gecko goed/went to see Elephant.

3. Elephant talks/talked to the fireflies last week.

4. The fireflies seed/saw Elephant coming.

5. Gecko sayed/said everything was okay.

Use the past tense of is or are in a sentence about Gecko.

Topic and Main Idea

Use a chart to write the topic and main idea of a nonfiction text.

Topic	Main idea

Use the chart to discuss the topic and main idea with a partner.

Grammar

What Will Happen Next?

Grammar Rules Future Tense Verbs

- A **future tense verb** tells about an action that will happen later, or in the future.

- Add **will** before a verb in the simple form to make a future tense verb.

  Example: *That **will happen** tomorrow morning.*

Circle the future tense verbs.

1. How do you think the elk (will respond) to the tiger?

2. The elk will run away from its enemy.

3. If the elk stays, the tiger will hunt it.

4. How do you think the plover will react to the crocodile?

5. The plover will go in the crocodile's mouth!

6. The crocodile will watch the plover.

7. The plover will clean the crocodile's teeth.

8. Then the plover will fly away.

> **Write a new sentence using a future tense verb. Share your sentence with a partner. Have your partner identify the verb.**

Key Points Reading

"Odd Couples"

Listen as your teacher reads. Follow with your finger.

1
Life in the wild is difficult. Some animals pair up to help each other. Animals can help each other keep clean. Cleaner shrimp eat dead skin and pests off fish.

2
Some animals get a ride. The remora fish attaches itself to a shark. The shark gives the fish a ride. The fish eats the shark's leftover food.

3
Some animals share the same food. The honeyguide bird finds a beehive, and the ratel tears it open.

4
Some animals protect each other. The clownfish lives inside a sea anemone's tentacles. The sea anemone eats fish that try to eat the clownfish.

Grammar

Forming the Future Tense

Grammar Rules Future Tense Verbs

There are two ways to make a verb tell about the future.

1. Add **will** before a present tense verb.
   Example: *I **will** call you tomorrow.*

2. Add a phrase with **going to** before a verb in the simple form.
   Examples:

I	**am going to** respond.
You, We, They	**are going to** respond.
He, She, It	**is going to** respond.

Write each underlined verb in another way.

1. I will help you with your homework. ___am going to help___

2. You will learn about animal partners. _____

3. Each odd couple will amaze you. _____

4. Their actions will surprise you, too. _____

5. We will have fun talking about them! _____

> **Make a sentence with a future tense verb. Have a partner write the future tense verb in a different way.**

Vocabulary

Yes or No?

1. **Listen to the questions. Write the missing Key Word where it belongs in each sentence.**

2. **Listen to the questions again.**

3. **Write <u>yes</u> or <u>no</u> for each question.**

1. Do animals in the wild hide from ____danger____ ? ____Yes.____

2. Are cleaner shrimp and oxpeckers animal _____ ? _____

3. Can animals _____ each other? _____

4. Is a plover _____ to a honeyguide bird? _____

5. Are the clownfish and sea anemone _____ partners? _____

6. Does a badger have the _____ to help a coyote? _____

Reread and Retell

"Odd Couples"

Fill out the topic and main idea chart for "Odd Couples."

Topic:	**Main idea:** Animal partnerships help both animals survive.

Detail:
Cleaner shrimp keep other fish clean.

Detail:

 Use your topic and main idea chart to tell a partner about "Odd Couples."

Name _____   Date _____

Phonics Practice

Schwa Sound

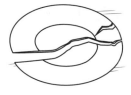

salad   broken   pencil   carrot

Read each word in the box and write it under the correct picture. Underline the letter in each word that has the schwa sound.

open	parrot	family	balloon

1.

_____

2.

_____

3.

_____

4.

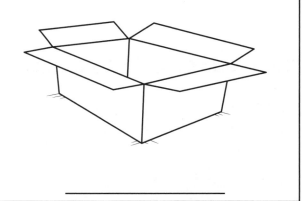

_____

Work with a partner. Take turns reading the question.

Can the family's parrot open the box with the balloon?

© Cengage Learning, Inc.

7.18

Unit 7 | Best Buddies

Fluency

"Odd Couples"

Use this passage to practice reading with proper intonation.

Like plovers, oxpeckers are birds. They ride on   8

giraffes, rhinos, and other big buddies.   14

The big animals don't mind. Why not? Well, the birds   24

eat bugs. That's good for the big animals. In return,   34

the birds get plenty of food. It's a perfect pairing!   44

From "Odd Couples," page 200

Intonation

B ☐ Does not change pitch.   A ☐ Changes pitch to match some of the content.

I ☐ Changes pitch, but does not match content.   AH ☐ Changes pitch to match all of the content.

Accuracy and Rate Formula

Use the formula to measure a reader's accuracy and rate while reading aloud.

_____ − _____ = _____
words attempted   number of errors   words correct per minute
in one minute   (wcpm)

"Working Together"

Make a K-W-L-Q chart as you read "Working Together."

K What I know	W What I want to learn	L What I learned	Q Questions I still have

👉 **Share your chart with a partner. Talk about how to find answers to the questions you still have after reading.**

Name _____ Date _____

Compare Topics and Main Ideas

Complete a comparison chart to compare "Odd Couples" and "Working Together."

Title	Topic	Main idea
"Odd Couples"		
"Working Together"		

Use the comparison chart to explain the topic and main idea of each selection.

Make-It-Future Tense Game

1. **Play with a partner.**

2. **Spin the spinner.**

3. **Change the verb by using the future tense. Say a sentence using the future tense verb.**

Make a Spinner

1. Place one loop of a paper clip over the center of the circle.

2. Push a sharp pencil through the loop and the paper.

3. Spin the paper clip around the pencil.

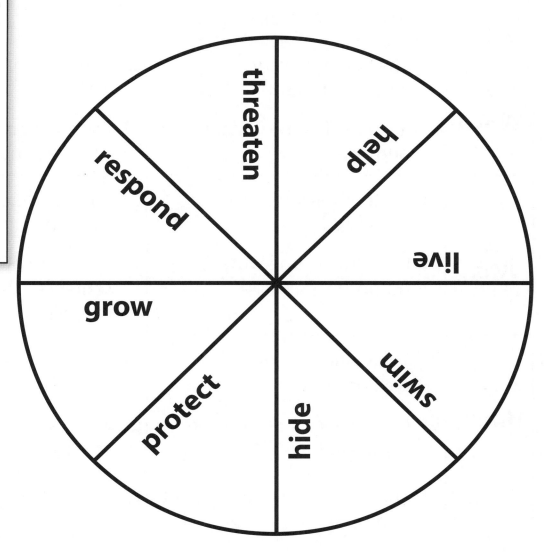

Organization

Writing is organized when it is easy to follow. All the ideas make sense together and flow from one idea to the next in an order that fits the writer's audience and purpose.

	Is the writing well-organized? Does it fit the writer's purpose?	**Does the writing flow?**
4 Wow!	❏ The writing is very well-organized. ❏ It clearly fits the writer's purpose.	❏ The writing is smooth and logical. ❏ Each sentence flows into the next one.
3 Ahh.	❏ Most of the writing is organized. ❏ It mostly fits the writer's purpose.	❏ Most of the writing is smooth. ❏ There are only a few sentences that do not flow logically.
2 Hmm.	❏ The writing is not well-organized. ❏ It fits the writer's purpose somewhat.	❏ Some of the writing is smooth. ❏ Many sentences do not flow smoothly.
1 Huh?	❏ The writing is not organized at all. ❏ It does not fit the writer's purpose.	❏ The writing is not smooth. ❏ The sentences do not flow smoothly or logically.

Writing Project

Topic, Main Idea, and Details Chart

Complete the chart for your report.

Topic:	
Main idea 1:	**Details:**
Main idea 2:	**Details:**
Main idea 3:	**Details:**
Main idea 4:	**Details:**

Revise

Use revision marks to make changes
to these paragraphs. Look for:
- details that support main ideas
- an order that makes sense

Revision Marks	
^	Add
℘	Take out
⌒⌐	Move to here

Crocodiles and Plovers

Plovers are small birds. They are not afraid of crocodiles.

A crocodile opens its mouth, and a plover hops in. The plover

eats the food stuck in the crocodile's teeth.

Crocodiles have teeth. Food gets stuck in their teeth.

Now the crocodile has a clean mouth!

Writing Project

Edit and Proofread

Use revision marks to edit and proofread these paragraphs.
Look for:

- commas after introductory words and phrases
- future tense with *going to* and *will*
- correct spelling

Revision Marks	
∧	Add
⌐	Take out
⬭ SP	Check spelling
⌄	Add comma

The Ratel and the Honeyguide

Ratels and honeyguides don't look like partners. However

they help each other get their favorite food—honey! What are

these creatures? Ratels are mammals and are also known as "honey

badgers." and Honeyguides are birds.

First the bird will flies over grasslands looking for beehives. When

it sees a hive, it make a noise.

If the ratel has heared the noise, it will rush to the hive. It uses its

sharp claws to tear open the hive. Sadly this is not good for the bees.

The ratel and honeyguide work well together. When they do, they

know they is goings to have a good meal!

Unit Concept Map

Our World

Make a concept map with the answers to the Big Question:
What does the world mean to you?

What does the world
mean to you?

Thinking Map

Character's Feelings

Make a character map to tell how a character feels and why.

Character	How the character feels	Why the character feels this way

Use your character map to tell a partner about a character's feelings in a story that you like.

© Cengage Learning, Inc.

Grammar

Where Are They?

Grammar Rules Prepositions

Prepositions tell where objects are.

Example: *The hamburgers are **on** a plate.*

1. Color objects that are <u>on</u> the table yellow.

2. Color objects that are <u>under</u> the table blue.

3. Color the object that is <u>beside</u> the table green.

4. Color the object that is <u>above</u> the table red.

Use prepositions to tell a partner where things are.

"Something to Write About"

Listen as your teacher reads. Follow with your finger.

1 Cheng wonders what to write to his pen pal. He makes dumplings with his mother. His grandmother says they are the best dumplings she has ever tasted.

2 The next morning, Cheng, his parents, and grandparents get ready for the Dragon Boat Festival. Then they all go to the harbor. They see lion dancing, hear music, and play games. Then they line up to watch the races.

3 Cheng's father competes in the Dragon Boat Race. He paddles as hard as he can. His boat glides across the finish line in front of the other boat.

4 Later, his family celebrates at their favorite restaurant. Cheng decides he will write a letter to his pen pal and tell him all about the Dragon Boat Festival.

Grammar

Spin and Move Game

1. Play with a partner.

2. Spin the spinner.

3. Say the word and use classroom objects to act out how things move.

4. The first player to correctly say and act out all six movements wins.

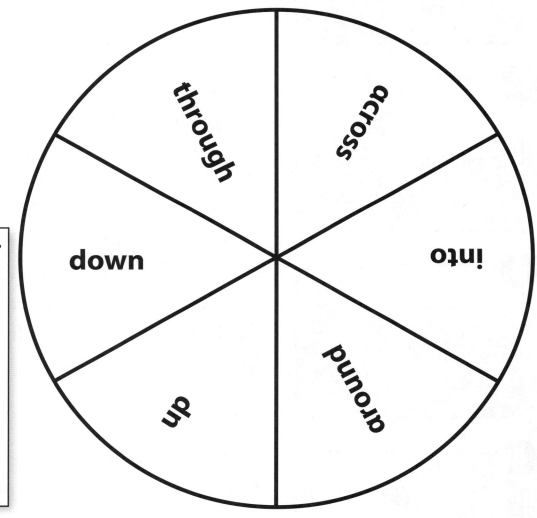

Make a Spinner

1. Place one loop of a paper clip over the center of the circle.

2. Push a sharp pencil through the loop and the paper.

3. Spin the paper clip around the pencil.

Name _____ Date _____

"Something to Write About"

Make a character map for the characters in "Something to Write About."

Character	How the character feels	Why the character feels this way
Cheng	Worried	He doesn't know what to write in the letter to his pen pal.

Use your character map to describe the story characters to a partner.

Suffixes: *-ly, -ness*

slow + ly = slowly	happy + ness = happiness

Read the word under each blank line. Add the correct ending. Write the new word on the line.

1. Her _____ made her cry.
          sad

2. The firefighter _____ climbed the ladder.
              brave

3. We have a _____ class at school.
            fit

4. Tom _____ gave the answer.
       glad

Work with a partner. Read the sentences aloud.

"Something to Write About"

Use this passage to practice reading with proper intonation.

Cheng read the letter from his pen pal in the United States.	12
Max wrote about the fun he would have this summer	22
during the 4th of July holiday.	28
Cheng worried. Would he have fun things to say in his reply?	40
"Come help me make dumplings," his mother called.	48
Cheng ran to the kitchen. His mother was making rice dumplings	59
wrapped in bamboo leaves for the Dragon Boat Festival.	68
Cheng loved those dumplings, with sweet bean paste or with meat.	79

From "Something to Write About," pages 234–235

Intonation

B ☐ Does not change pitch.   A ☐ Changes pitch to match some of the content.

I ☐ Changes pitch, but does not match content.   AH ☐ Changes pitch to match all of the content.

Accuracy and Rate Formula

Use the formula to measure a reader's accuracy and rate while reading aloud.

$$\underline{\hspace{3cm}} - \underline{\hspace{3cm}} = \underline{\hspace{3cm}}$$

words attempted in one minute	number of errors	words corrected per minute (wcpm)

Compare Language

Compare the language in "Something to Write About" and "Our World Is Many Shades." Write what the sentences or phrases mean.

"Something to Write About"	"Our World Is Many Shades"
Cheng ran to the kitchen. *This means exactly what it says.*	Our world is many shades of the languages we speak. *Meaning: There are many languages in the world.*
	We find a way to listen to others' stories. *Meaning:*

▰▰▰▰▰ **Take turns with a partner. Explain which words mean exactly what they say and which words do not.**

Grammar

An American Restaurant

Grammar Rules Prepositions

Some **prepositions** show location.
Examples: *in, on, above, over, below, under, beside, next to*

Some **prepositions** show direction.
Examples: *up, down, through, across, into, around*

Circle the word to complete each sentence. Then read the sentence.

1. The pot is under/on the stove.

2. Dad puts noodles into/across the pot.

3. I stand next to/above Dad.

4. I stir the noodles around/down with a spoon.

5. The flag is beside/through the stove.

Write a sentence that includes a preposition. Share your sentence with a partner.

Thinking Map

Author's Purpose

Make an author's purpose chart to tell about a nonfiction text you have read.

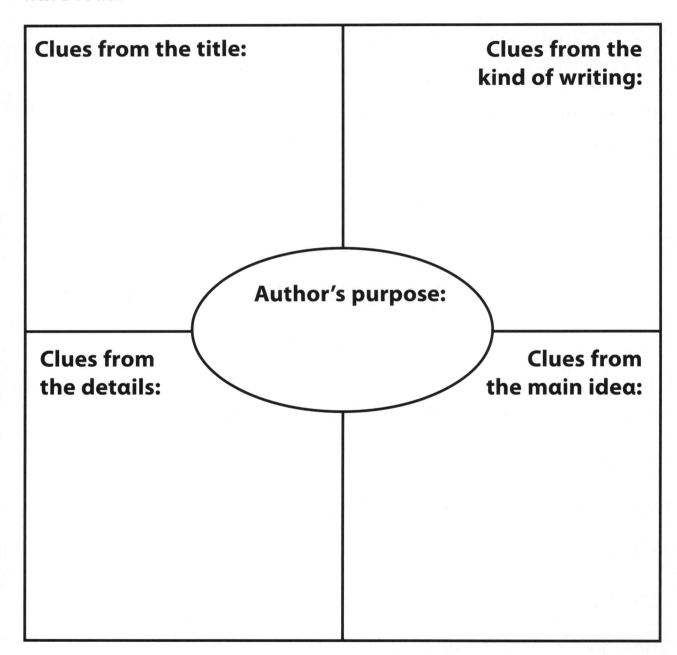

Clues from the title:

Clues from the kind of writing:

Author's purpose:

Clues from the details:

Clues from the main idea:

▸ Share your chart with a partner and compare the author's purpose.

Name _____   Date _____

Happy Fourth of February!

Grammar Rules Prepositions

A **preposition** can tell when something happens.

Examples:

- *We went to the National Park **before** summer.*
- *We went hiking **after** the sunrise.*
- *We ate trail mix **during** our hike.*

Circle the preposition in each sentence.

1. Sri Lanka's Independence Day is on February 4th.

2. We celebrate our country's independence in our capital, Colombo.

3. Everyone packs a picnic before the celebration.

4. My family gathers together at the beach.

5. We eat dinner during sunset.

6. Then we go to an outdoor concert after dark.

7. It is another year until the next celebration.

 Choose a sentence and change the preposition. Share your new sentence with a partner. Tell how the new preposition changes the meaning of the sentence.

Name _____   Date _____

"An Eagle's Eye"

Listen as your teacher reads. Follow with your finger.

1

Eagles fly across our skies. They look down and see different parts of the world.

One sees the Great Barrier Reef of Australia. Another eagle sees the white shores of Borneo.

2

Other eagles visit the Great Wall of China, Mount Everest, the Caspian Sea, and the ancient city of Petra.

3

A crowned eagle flies over the Zambezi River. A bald eagle is united with the Northern Lights of Alaska. A golden eagle flies south over the continent of North America.

4

All around the world, eagles look down at the cities and landforms below them. They tell us to enjoy the natural beauty of our earth and to admire the monuments of its people.

Grammar

Holidays Around the Year

Grammar Rules Prepositional Phrases

A **prepositional phrase** tells more about something in the sentence.
- It begins with a preposition.
- It ends with a noun or a pronoun.

Underline the prepositional phrase in each sentence. Circle each preposition.

1. America has many national holidays (during) the year.

2. The country celebrates New Year's Day on January 1st.

3. President's Day is in February.

4. Memorial Day became a holiday after the American Civil War.

5. Most schools start summer vacation before July 4th.

6. Then there is not another holiday until September.

7. People celebrate Labor Day with parades.

8. Everyone is grateful at Thanksgiving.

Make a sentence about another holiday you know. Use a prepositional phrase in your sentence. Share your sentence with a partner.

Name _____ Date _____

"An Eagle's Eye"

Make an author's purpose chart. Figure out the author's purpose for writing "An Eagle's Eye."

Clues from the title:

"An Eagle's Eye"

The selection is about what eagles see in the world.

Clues from the kind of writing:

Literary nonfiction presents facts and ideas in an interesting way.

Author's purpose

Clues from the details:

Clues from the main idea:

 Work with a partner. Compare the author's purposes that you found.

© Cengage Learning, Inc.

Suffixes: -ful, -less

| bowl + ful = bowlful | shoe + less = shoeless |

Read the word below each blank line. Add the correct ending. Write the new word on the line.

1. My dog is very _____ .
   play

2. The _____ chair is not comfortable.
   arm

3. We always try to be _____ .
   help

4. I have a _____ picture book.
   word

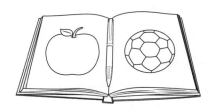

Work with a partner. Read the sentences aloud.

Fluency

"An Eagle's Eye"

Use this passage to practice reading with proper phrasing.

Crossing the mountains of Mexico,	5
a black hawk eagle flies	10
towards the magnificent ruins of Chichén Itzá.	17
It was the ceremonial capital of the Mayan civilization.	26
Enormous pyramids rise above the forest around it.	34
Snakes and jaguars decorate its walls.	40
They are symbols of a great past.	47
The black-and-white hawk eagle	53
flies seeking the South American winds.	59
He finds a blanket of forest below him, crossing into Brazil.	70
It is the great Amazon rain forest.	77
It is a celebration of nature.	83
The calls of its wildlife unite,	89
welcoming the eagle to their home.	95

From "An Eagle's Eye," pages 277–278

Phrasing

B ☐ Rarely pauses while reading the text.   A ☐ Frequently pauses at appropriate points in the text.

I ☐ Occasionally pauses while reading the text.   AH ☐ Consistently pauses at all appropriate points in the text.

Accuracy and Rate Formula

Use the formula to measure a reader's accuracy and rate while reading aloud.

$$\underline{\hspace{3cm}} - \underline{\hspace{3cm}} = \underline{\hspace{3cm}}$$

words attempted   number of errors   words corrected per
in one minute   minute (wcpm)

Name _____ Date _____

"This Land Is Your Land"

On each card, write an unfamiliar word, what you think it means, and clues to its meaning.

WORD DETECTIVE

New word: _____

What I think it means: _____

_____

🔍 Clues: _____

_____

📖 Definition: _____

_____

WORD DETECTIVE

New word: _____

What I think it means: _____

_____

🔍 Clues: _____

_____

📖 Definition: _____

_____

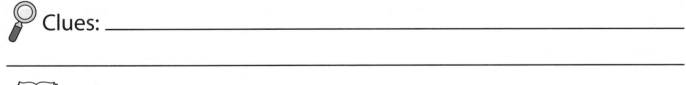

After you have finished reading, use a dictionary to find the definition of the word. Share your work with a partner.

Compare Author's Purpose

Make a comparison chart. Show how "An Eagle's Eye" and "This Land Is Your Land" are the same and how they are different.

	"An Eagle's Eye" by Anna Goy	"This Land Is Your Land" by Woody Guthrie
persuade readers		✓
inform readers	✓	
entertain readers		
share experiences		
express feelings		
express creativity		

▬▬▬ **Share your chart with a partner. Take turns comparing the authors' purposes in each selection.**

Grammar

Do These Details Fit?

1. Point to a sentence starter.

2. Have a partner point to a prepositional phrase.

3. If the cards make a clear sentence, color in the squares. If not, begin again.

4. Play until all the squares are colored.

Sentences

Sentence Starters

We go _____ .	Teresa and I write _____ .	Koji and Lynn have fun _____ .	You and I read _____ .

Prepositional Phrases

to the park	after breakfast	during the concert	into the monument
along the coast	with the map	about world history	under the blue sky

Voice

Every writer has a special way of saying things, or a voice. The voice should sound genuine, or real, and be unique to that writer.

	Does the tone, formal or informal, fit the purpose and audience?	Does the writing sound genuine to the writer?
4 **Wow!**	❏ The writer's tone fits the purpose and audience.	❏ The writing is genuine. It shows who the writer is.
3 **Ahh.**	❏ The writer's tone mostly fits the purpose and audience.	❏ Most of the writing sounds genuine.
2 **Hmm.**	❏ Some of the writing fits the purpose and audience. Some does not.	❏ Some of the writing sounds genuine.
1 **Huh?**	❏ The writer's tone does not fit the purpose and audience.	❏ The writing does not sound genuine.

Feelings Chart

Complete a chart for your personal narrative.

Person	How the person feels	Why the person feels this way

Writing Project

Revise

Use revision marks to make changes to these paragraphs. Look for:

- words and sentences that sound like you
- details that tell why the event was important

Revision Marks	
^	Add
ℐ	Take out

Our Class Party

A few weeks ago, my class had a party. People brought food that their families had made. I brought some things and my friends brought some other things. The food all smelled amazing, and it made me. There was food there that I had never seen before.

This party was important to me. It showed me how people from different cultures can here we become one culture, through food and other shared interests.

Writing Project

Edit and Proofread

Use revision marks to edit and proofread these paragraphs.
Look for:

- misspelled words
- paragraph indents
- correct prepositions and prepositional phrases

Revision Marks	
∧	Add
ℱ	Take out
⬭ SP	Check spelling
⌐	Indent

A New Life in America

My class went to Ellis Island. Until 1954, Ellis Island was where many

European immigrants first entered America. We learned about all

the people who came by America looking for freedom.

Many of these people had no money. All of there possessions

were under one or too suitcases. They could not read or rite English.

America is a place where people can start a new life. That's what

America means to me.

Photographic Credits

6.14 (t) Angus McComiskey/Alamy Stock Photo. (tc) Alexis TOUREAU/Getty Images. (bc) Elena-Grishina/ Shutterstock.com. (b) Angus McComiskey/Alamy Stock Photo. 7.14 (t) Tim Laman/National Geographic Image Collection. (tc) Reinhard Dirscherl/WaterFrame/Getty Images. (bc) NIGEL DENNIS/Science Source. (b) Stephen Frink/Photodisc/Getty Images. 8.13 (t) StockIllustrations.com/Alamy Stock Photo. (tc) Travel Wild/Alamy Stock Photo. (bc) NortePhoto/Alamy Stock Photo. (b) Octavio Campos Salles/Alamy Stock Photo.